THE ADVANCED GRABOVOI CODES

REFERENCE

Volume II — Biological & Nervous System

CRP Structural Codes™ System

300–350 Tiered, Indexed & Classified Sequences

A Classified System for Nervous System Regulation,

Sleep Architecture & Biological Stability

James Hutchinson

DISCLAIMER

The numerical sequences presented in this book are organized within the CRP Structural Codes™ framework. They are provided as cognitive structuring tools for focus, regulation, and disciplined application.

This work does not claim to cure disease, guarantee outcomes, or replace professional care.

Use responsibly.

SYSTEM NOTICE

Each sequence follows the structural format:

DD SS F I VV C

DD — Domain
SS — Subsystem
F — Function
I — Intensity
VV — Variant
C — Check Digit

Function Types:

1 — Stabilize
2 — Increase
3 — Decrease
4 — Repair
5 — Protect
6 — Amplify
7 — Recalibrate
8 — Accelerate

Intensity Classes:

Class I — Gentle Calibration
Class II — Standard Structural Activation
Class III — High-Intensity Structural Shift
Class IV — Reserved

HOW TO USE THIS VOLUME

1. Identify the primary physiological instability (sleep, stress load, overstimulation, fatigue, recovery).
2. Select the appropriate subsystem.
3. Choose the function type required.
4. Select an intensity class appropriate to your current stability level.
5. Apply no more than three concurrent sequences.
6. Stabilize before accelerating.
7. Reduce overload before amplifying capacity.

This is a structured reference system. Apply with discipline.

TABLE OF CONTENTS

PART II — INDEX ARCHITECTURE

APPENDICES

INTRODUCTION

Most health content is advice.

This is architecture.

The Advanced Grabovoi Codes Reference — Volume II: Biological & Nervous System is a structured CRP Structural Codes™ system designed to organize numerical sequences into classified subsystems for regulation, recovery, and biological stability.

This volume emphasizes nervous system regulation, sleep architecture optimization, stress-load control, recovery pacing, and physiological resilience.

It is not a promise of cure.

It is a disciplined reference framework intended to support structured focus and consistent application.

Volume II contains 300–350 classified sequences organized across 15 biological subsystems.

This is not a motivational wellness book.

It is a reference manual.

01-01 Nervous System Regulation

Domain 01 — Biological Systems

Focus:

- Autonomic balance
- Hyperarousal reduction
- Freeze response recalibration
- Stress recovery pacing
- Baseline stabilization

Entry 1

Structural Code: **101120114**
Catalog ID: CRP-01-01-0001
Function: Stabilize (1)
Intensity: Class II
Variant: 01

Autonomic Balance Anchor

Stabilizes sympathetic–parasympathetic interaction.

Entry 2

Structural Code: **101220127**
Function: Increase (2)

Intensity: Class II
Variant: 02

Parasympathetic Activation Increase

Supports calm-state accessibility.

Entry 3

Structural Code: **101320135**
Function: Decrease (3)
Intensity: Class I
Variant: 03

Hyperarousal Reduction

Reduces excessive stress activation patterns.

Entry 4

Structural Code: **101420146**
Function: Repair (4)
Intensity: Class II
Variant: 04

Stress Recovery Reset

Restores post-stress equilibrium.

Entry 5

Structural Code: **101520153**
Function: Protect (5)
Intensity: Class II
Variant: 05

Nervous System Protection Shield

Reinforces resilience during environmental stress.

Entry 6

Structural Code: **101620169**
Function: Amplify (6)
Intensity: Class II
Variant: 06

Regulation Capacity Amplifier

Strengthens adaptive stress response.

Entry 7

Structural Code: **101720176**
Function: Recalibrate (7)

Intensity: Class I
Variant: 07

Baseline Arousal Calibration

Aligns activation level with situational demand.

Entry 8

Structural Code: **101820188**
Function: Accelerate (8)
Intensity: Class I
Variant: 08

Calm-State Access Acceleration

Improves transition into regulated states.

Entry 9

Structural Code: **101220194**
Function: Increase (2)
Intensity: Class III
Variant: 09

High-Level Nervous Stability Surge

Advanced reinforcement of calm-state endurance.

Entry 10

Structural Code: **101320203**
Function: Decrease (3)
Intensity: Class II
Variant: 10

Stress Reactivity Reduction

Reduces exaggerated response cycles.

Entry 11

Structural Code: **101520214**
Function: Protect (5)
Intensity: Class III
Variant: 11

Autonomic Integrity Lock

Deep reinforcement of stable baseline regulation.

Entry 12

Structural Code: **101620227**
Function: Amplify (6)
Intensity: Class II
Variant: 12

Adaptive Recovery Amplifier

Improves return-to-baseline speed.

Entry 13

Structural Code: **101420236**
Function: Repair (4)
Intensity: Class I
Variant: 13

Overload Recovery Reset

Supports stabilization after overstimulation.

Entry 14

Structural Code: **101720245**
Function: Recalibrate (7)
Intensity: Class II
Variant: 14

Fight–Flight Calibration

Aligns threat perception with actual context.

Entry 15

Structural Code: **101120254**
Function: Stabilize (1)
Intensity: Class I
Variant: 15

Baseline Nervous Stability Anchor

Reinforces steady daily regulation.

Entry 16

Structural Code: **101820263**
Function: Accelerate (8)
Intensity: Class II
Variant: 16

Recovery Speed Boost

Enhances stress recovery efficiency.

Entry 17

Structural Code: **101220272**
Function: Increase (2)
Intensity: Class II
Variant: 17

Emotional Regulation Capacity Increase

Supports steadier mood under load.

Entry 18

Structural Code: **101320281**
Function: Decrease (3)
Intensity: Class II
Variant: 18

Freeze Response Sensitivity Reduction

Reduces immobilization patterns.

Entry 19

Structural Code: **101620296**
Function: Amplify (6)
Intensity: Class I
Variant: 19

Calm-State Reinforcement

Strengthens repeated regulated-state access.

Entry 20

Structural Code: **101520305**
Function: Protect (5)
Intensity: Class III
Variant: 20

Nervous System Sovereignty Anchor

Deep reinforcement of long-term autonomic stability.

01-02 Sleep Architecture Optimization

Domain 01 — Biological Systems

Focus:
- Sleep onset stability
- Deep sleep reinforcement
- REM balance
- Circadian calibration
- Night waking reduction
- Sleep continuity protection

Entry 1

Structural Code: **102120114**
Catalog ID: CRP-01-02-0001
Function: Stabilize (1)
Intensity: Class II
Variant: 01

Sleep Onset Stability Anchor

Stabilizes transition into sleep.

Entry 2

Structural Code: **102220127**
Function: Increase (2)

Intensity: Class II
Variant: 02

Deep Sleep Capacity Increase

Supports deeper sleep availability.

Entry 3

Structural Code: **102320135**
Function: Decrease (3)
Intensity: Class I
Variant: 03

Night Waking Reduction

Reduces repeated awakening patterns.

Entry 4

Structural Code: **102420146**
Function: Repair (4)
Intensity: Class II
Variant: 04

Sleep Disruption Recovery Reset

Restores stability after poor sleep cycles.

Entry 5

Structural Code: **102520153**
Function: Protect (5)
Intensity: Class II
Variant: 05

Sleep Continuity Protection Shield

Protects uninterrupted sleep architecture.

Entry 6

Structural Code: **102620169**
Function: Amplify (6)
Intensity: Class II
Variant: 06

Circadian Signal Amplifier

Strengthens day–night rhythm consistency.

Entry 7

Structural Code: **102720176**
Function: Recalibrate (7)

Intensity: Class I
Variant: 07

Sleep Timing Calibration

Aligns sleep timing with stable rhythm.

Entry 8

Structural Code: **102820188**
Function: Accelerate (8)
Intensity: Class I
Variant: 08

Sleep Onset Acceleration

Improves speed of sleep entry.

Entry 9

Structural Code: **102220194**
Function: Increase (2)
Intensity: Class III
Variant: 09

High-Depth Sleep Surge

Advanced reinforcement of restorative sleep depth.

Entry 10

Structural Code: **102320203**
Function: Decrease (3)
Intensity: Class II
Variant: 10

Pre-Sleep Overthinking Reduction

Reduces cognitive activation at bedtime.

Entry 11

Structural Code: **102520214**
Function: Protect (5)
Intensity: Class III
Variant: 11

Sleep Architecture Integrity Lock

Deep protection of sleep structure.

Entry 12

Structural Code: **102620227**
Function: Amplify (6)

Intensity: Class II
Variant: 12

Recovery Sleep Amplifier

Improves restorative quality after strain.

Entry 13

Structural Code: **102420236**
Function: Repair (4)
Intensity: Class I
Variant: 13

Circadian Drift Recovery

Restores rhythm after schedule disruption.

Entry 14

Structural Code: **102720245**
Function: Recalibrate (7)
Intensity: Class II
Variant: 14

REM Balance Calibration

Supports balanced REM expression.

Entry 15

Structural Code: **102120254**
Function: Stabilize (1)
Intensity: Class I
Variant: 15

Night Routine Stability Anchor

Reinforces consistent sleep preparation behavior.

Entry 16

Structural Code: **102820263**
Function: Accelerate (8)
Intensity: Class II
Variant: 16

Sleep Recovery Speed Boost

Improves rebound after sleep debt.

Entry 17

Structural Code: **102220272**
Function: Increase (2)
Intensity: Class II
Variant: 17

Sleep Consistency Increase

Strengthens stable nightly rhythm.

Entry 18

Structural Code: **102320281**
Function: Decrease (3)
Intensity: Class II
Variant: 18

Early Morning Waking Reduction

Reduces premature waking patterns.

Entry 19

Structural Code: **102620296**
Function: Amplify (6)
Intensity: Class I
Variant: 19

Parasympathetic Sleep Reinforcement

Strengthens calm-state dominance during sleep.

Entry 20

Structural Code: **102520305**
Function: Protect (5)
Intensity: Class III
Variant: 20

Long-Form Sleep Continuity Anchor

Deep reinforcement of stable, uninterrupted sleep.

01-03 Stress Hormone Stabilization

Domain 01 — Biological Systems

Focus:
- Cortisol rhythm stability
- Stress-load containment
- Adrenal pacing
- Recovery after stress
- Fight/flight reduction
- Baseline restoration

Entry 1

Structural Code: **103120114**
Catalog ID: CRP-01-03-0001
Function: Stabilize (1)
Intensity: Class II
Variant: 01

Cortisol Rhythm Stability Anchor

Stabilizes daily stress-hormone rhythm.

Entry 2

Structural Code: **103220127**
Function: Increase (2)
Intensity: Class II
Variant: 02

Recovery Hormone Balance Increase

Supports stable recovery pacing.

Entry 3

Structural Code: **103320135**
Function: Decrease (3)
Intensity: Class I
Variant: 03

Stress Hormone Spike Reduction

Reduces sudden stress surges.

Entry 4

Structural Code: **103420146**
Function: Repair (4)
Intensity: Class II
Variant: 04

Adrenal Load Recovery Reset

Restores stability after prolonged stress load.

Entry 5

Structural Code: **103520153**
Function: Protect (5)
Intensity: Class II
Variant: 05

Stress Buffer Protection Shield

Protects recovery capacity during pressure.

Entry 6

Structural Code: **103620169**
Function: Amplify (6)
Intensity: Class II
Variant: 06

Recovery Capacity Amplifier

Strengthens ability to return to baseline.

Entry 7

Structural Code: **103720176**
Function: Recalibrate (7)
Intensity: Class I
Variant: 07

Stress Response Calibration

Aligns reaction intensity to real demand.

Entry 8

Structural Code: **103820188**
Function: Accelerate (8)
Intensity: Class I
Variant: 08

Downshift Acceleration

Improves speed of calming after stress.

Entry 9

Structural Code: **103220194**
Function: Increase (2)
Intensity: Class III
Variant: 09

High-Resilience Hormone Stability Surge

Advanced reinforcement of stress tolerance.

Entry 10

Structural Code: **103320203**
Function: Decrease (3)
Intensity: Class II
Variant: 10

Cortisol Noise Reduction

Reduces background stress activation.

Entry 11

Structural Code: **103520214**
Function: Protect (5)
Intensity: Class III
Variant: 11

Adrenal Integrity Lock

Deep protection of stress recovery systems.

Entry 12

Structural Code: **103620227**
Function: Amplify (6)

Intensity: Class II
Variant: 12

Baseline Restoration Amplifier

Improves consistency of stable mood/energy baseline.

Entry 13

Structural Code: **103420236**
Function: Repair (4)
Intensity: Class I
Variant: 13

Stress Exhaustion Recovery

Supports stabilization after burnout phases.

Entry 14

Structural Code: **103720245**
Function: Recalibrate (7)
Intensity: Class II
Variant: 14

Threat Perception Calibration

Reduces false-alarm activation.

Entry 15

Structural Code: **103120254**
Function: Stabilize (1)
Intensity: Class I
Variant: 15

Daily Stress Rhythm Anchor

Reinforces stable day pacing.

Entry 16

Structural Code: **103820263**
Function: Accelerate (8)
Intensity: Class II
Variant: 16

Recovery Cycle Speed Boost

Improves bounce-back after pressure events.

Entry 17

Structural Code: **103220272**
Function: Increase (2)
Intensity: Class II
Variant: 17

Calm-State Access Increase

Strengthens shift into regulation.

Entry 18

Structural Code: **103320281**
Function: Decrease (3)
Intensity: Class II
Variant: 18

Tension Load Reduction

Reduces body-held stress accumulation.

Entry 19

Structural Code: **103620296**
Function: Amplify (6)
Intensity: Class I
Variant: 19

Resilience Reinforcement

Strengthens long-term stress tolerance.

Entry 20

Structural Code: **103520305**
Function: Protect (5)

Intensity: Class III
Variant: 20

Stress Sovereignty Anchor

Deep reinforcement of long-term stress-hormone stability.

01-04 Inflammatory Response Regulation

Domain 01 — Biological Systems

Focus:
- Systemic inflammation reduction support
- Recovery reinforcement
- Reactivity stabilization
- Load containment
- Baseline resilience

Entry 1

Structural Code: **104120114**
Catalog ID: CRP-01-04-0001
Function: Stabilize (1)
Intensity: Class II
Variant: 01

Inflammation Stability Anchor

Supports stable inflammatory response behavior.

Entry 2

Structural Code: **104220127**
Function: Increase (2)

Intensity: Class II
Variant: 02

Recovery Resilience Increase

Supports steadier recovery pacing.

Entry 3

Structural Code: **104320135**
Function: Decrease (3)
Intensity: Class I
Variant: 03

Reactivity Reduction

Reduces excess inflammatory reactivity patterns.

Entry 4

Structural Code: **104420146**
Function: Repair (4)
Intensity: Class II
Variant: 04

Post-Inflammation Recovery Reset

Supports recovery after overload states.

Entry 5

Structural Code: **104520153**
Function: Protect (5)
Intensity: Class II
Variant: 05

Recovery Protection Shield

Protects stability during strain.

Entry 6

Structural Code: **104620169**
Function: Amplify (6)
Intensity: Class II
Variant: 06

Repair Capacity Amplifier

Strengthens recovery orientation.

Entry 7

Structural Code: **104720176**
Function: Recalibrate (7)
Intensity: Class I
Variant: 07

Immune Reactivity Calibration

Aligns response intensity with real demand.

Entry 8

Structural Code: **104820188**
Function: Accelerate (8)
Intensity: Class I
Variant: 08

Recovery Downshift Acceleration

Improves speed of return toward stability.

Entry 9

Structural Code: **104220194**
Function: Increase (2)
Intensity: Class III
Variant: 09

High-Resilience Recovery Surge

Advanced reinforcement of recovery capacity.

Entry 10

Structural Code: **104320203**
Function: Decrease (3)
Intensity: Class II
Variant: 10

Background Inflammation Load Reduction

Reduces persistent low-grade reactivity patterns.

Entry 11

Structural Code: **104520214**
Function: Protect (5)
Intensity: Class III
Variant: 11

Inflammatory Integrity Lock

Deep protection of baseline stability.

Entry 12

Structural Code: **104620227**
Function: Amplify (6)
Intensity: Class II
Variant: 12

Cellular Recovery Amplifier

Supports stabilization of repair orientation.

Entry 13

Structural Code: **104420236**
Function: Repair (4)
Intensity: Class I
Variant: 13

Flare Recovery Reset

Supports recovery after inflammatory flare patterns.

Entry 14

Structural Code: **104720245**
Function: Recalibrate (7)
Intensity: Class II
Variant: 14

Sensitivity Threshold Calibration

Adjusts reactivity threshold toward stability.

Entry 15

Structural Code: **104120254**
Function: Stabilize (1)
Intensity: Class I
Variant: 15

Daily Recovery Stability Anchor

Reinforces consistent recovery rhythm.

Entry 16

Structural Code: **104820263**
Function: Accelerate (8)
Intensity: Class II
Variant: 16

Repair Cycle Speed Boost

Improves recovery pacing after load.

Entry 17

Structural Code: **104220272**
Function: Increase (2)
Intensity: Class II
Variant: 17

Resilience Baseline Increase

Strengthens general recovery stability.

Entry 18

Structural Code: **104320281**
Function: Decrease (3)
Intensity: Class II
Variant: 18

Pain-Inflammation Loop Reduction

Reduces reactive loop reinforcement.

Entry 19

Structural Code: **104620296**
Function: Amplify (6)
Intensity: Class I
Variant: 19

Anti-Reactivity Reinforcement

Strengthens stable response habits.

Entry 20

Structural Code: **104520305**
Function: Protect (5)
Intensity: Class III
Variant: 20

Long-Term Recovery Sovereignty Anchor

Deep reinforcement of stable inflammatory regulation.

01-05 Energy Metabolism Optimization

Domain 01 — Biological Systems

Focus:
- Daytime energy stability
- Fatigue reduction
- Metabolic rhythm support
- Energy crash prevention
- Output consistency
- Recovery pacing

Entry 1

Structural Code: **105120114**
Catalog ID: CRP-01-05-0001
Function: Stabilize (1)
Intensity: Class II
Variant: 01

Daytime Energy Stability Anchor

Stabilizes baseline energy across the day.

Entry 2

Structural Code: **105220127**
Function: Increase (2)
Intensity: Class II
Variant: 02

Energy Availability Increase

Supports consistent access to usable energy.

Entry 3

Structural Code: **105320135**
Function: Decrease (3)
Intensity: Class I
Variant: 03

Fatigue Load Reduction

Reduces persistent low-energy patterns.

Entry 4

Structural Code: **105420146**
Function: Repair (4)
Intensity: Class II
Variant: 04

Crash-Recovery Reset

Restores stability after energy crashes.

Entry 5

Structural Code: **105520153**
Function: Protect (5)
Intensity: Class II
Variant: 05

Energy Reserve Protection Shield

Protects baseline energy from depletion.

Entry 6

Structural Code: **105620169**
Function: Amplify (6)
Intensity: Class II
Variant: 06

Metabolic Efficiency Amplifier

Strengthens output-to-energy ratio.

Entry 7

Structural Code: **105720176**
Function: Recalibrate (7)

Intensity: Class I
Variant: 07

Energy Rhythm Calibration

Aligns energy peaks and troughs toward stability.

Entry 8

Structural Code: **105820188**
Function: Accelerate (8)
Intensity: Class I
Variant: 08

Recovery Energy Acceleration

Improves speed of energy restoration.

Entry 9

Structural Code: **105220194**
Function: Increase (2)
Intensity: Class III
Variant: 09

High-Output Energy Surge

Advanced reinforcement of sustained energy capacity.

Entry 10

Structural Code: **105320203**
Function: Decrease (3)
Intensity: Class II
Variant: 10

Energy Leak Reduction

Reduces drain patterns that consume baseline energy.

Entry 11

Structural Code: **105520214**
Function: Protect (5)
Intensity: Class III
Variant: 11

Metabolic Stability Lock

Deep protection of stable energy systems.

Entry 12

Structural Code: **105620227**
Function: Amplify (6)
Intensity: Class II
Variant: 12

Recovery Efficiency Amplifier

Strengthens restoration after exertion.

Entry 13

Structural Code: **105420236**
Function: Repair (4)
Intensity: Class I
Variant: 13

Overexertion Recovery Reset

Supports stabilization after pushing too hard.

Entry 14

Structural Code: **105720245**
Function: Recalibrate (7)
Intensity: Class II
Variant: 14

Appetite–Energy Calibration

Aligns intake signals with stable energy needs.

Entry 15

Structural Code: **105120254**
Function: Stabilize (1)

Intensity: Class I
Variant: 15

Daily Energy Consistency Anchor

Reinforces reliable energy pacing.

Entry 16

Structural Code: **105820263**
Function: Accelerate (8)
Intensity: Class II
Variant: 16

Fatigue Recovery Speed Boost

Improves rebound after low-energy episodes.

Entry 17

Structural Code: **105220272**
Function: Increase (2)
Intensity: Class II
Variant: 17

Stamina Capacity Increase

Supports sustained effort without crash.

Entry 18

Structural Code: **105320281**
Function: Decrease (3)
Intensity: Class II
Variant: 18

Afternoon Crash Reduction

Reduces predictable mid-day drops.

Entry 19

Structural Code: **105620296**
Function: Amplify (6)
Intensity: Class I
Variant: 19

Metabolic Discipline Reinforcement

Strengthens stable daily metabolic habits.

Entry 20

Structural Code: **105520305**
Function: Protect (5)

Intensity: Class III
Variant: 20

Long-Term Energy Sovereignty Anchor

Deep reinforcement of stable, durable energy baseline.

01-06 Hormonal Structuring

Domain 01 — Biological Systems

Focus:
- Endocrine rhythm support
- Hormonal volatility stabilization
- Circadian–hormone alignment
- Recovery pacing support
- Baseline consistency

Entry 1

Structural Code: **106120114**
Catalog ID: CRP-01-06-0001
Function: Stabilize (1)
Intensity: Class II
Variant: 01

Endocrine Rhythm Stability Anchor

Supports stable hormonal rhythm behavior.

Entry 2

Structural Code: **106220127**
Function: Increase (2)

Intensity: Class II
Variant: 02

Hormonal Balance Capacity Increase

Supports steadier internal regulation.

Entry 3

Structural Code: **106320135**
Function: Decrease (3)
Intensity: Class I
Variant: 03

Volatility Reduction

Reduces hormonal fluctuation patterns.

Entry 4

Structural Code: **106420146**
Function: Repair (4)
Intensity: Class II
Variant: 04

Rhythm Disruption Recovery Reset

Supports stabilization after irregular cycles.

Entry 5

Structural Code: **106520153**
Function: Protect (5)
Intensity: Class II
Variant: 05

Endocrine Stability Protection Shield

Protects baseline regulation under load.

Entry 6

Structural Code: **106620169**
Function: Amplify (6)
Intensity: Class II
Variant: 06

Regulation Efficiency Amplifier

Strengthens consistency of internal balance habits.

Entry 7

Structural Code: **106720176**
Function: Recalibrate (7)
Intensity: Class I
Variant: 07

Hormone Rhythm Calibration

Aligns internal rhythms toward stability.

Entry 8

Structural Code: **106820188**
Function: Accelerate (8)
Intensity: Class I
Variant: 08

Balance Restoration Acceleration

Improves speed of return toward steadier rhythm.

Entry 9

Structural Code: **106220194**
Function: Increase (2)
Intensity: Class III
Variant: 09

High-Stability Balance Surge

Advanced reinforcement of endocrine steadiness.

Entry 10

Structural Code: **106320203**
Function: Decrease (3)
Intensity: Class II
Variant: 10

Stress-Driven Hormone Noise Reduction

Reduces stress-linked volatility patterns.

Entry 11

Structural Code: **106520214**
Function: Protect (5)
Intensity: Class III
Variant: 11

Endocrine Integrity Lock

Deep protection of stable baseline rhythm.

Entry 12

Structural Code: **106620227**
Function: Amplify (6)
Intensity: Class II
Variant: 12

Recovery Rhythm Amplifier

Supports steady restoration pacing.

Entry 13

Structural Code: **106420236**
Function: Repair (4)
Intensity: Class I
Variant: 13

Volatility Recovery Reset

Supports stabilization after fluctuation cycles.

Entry 14

Structural Code: **106720245**
Function: Recalibrate (7)
Intensity: Class II
Variant: 14

Circadian–Hormone Alignment Calibration

Aligns day–night rhythm with internal balance.

Entry 15

Structural Code: **106120254**
Function: Stabilize (1)
Intensity: Class I
Variant: 15

Daily Balance Consistency Anchor

Reinforces reliable internal pacing.

Entry 16

Structural Code: **106820263**
Function: Accelerate (8)
Intensity: Class II
Variant: 16

Regulation Recovery Speed Boost

Improves bounce-back after imbalance periods.

Entry 17

Structural Code: **106220272**
Function: Increase (2)
Intensity: Class II
Variant: 17

Regulation Capacity Increase

Supports steadier baseline maintenance.

Entry 18

Structural Code: **106320281**
Function: Decrease (3)
Intensity: Class II
Variant: 18

Sensitivity Load Reduction

Reduces reactivity during hormonal fluctuation windows.

Entry 19

Structural Code: **106620296**
Function: Amplify (6)
Intensity: Class I
Variant: 19

Stability Habit Reinforcement

Strengthens consistent regulation behavior.

Entry 20

Structural Code: **106520305**
Function: Protect (5)
Intensity: Class III
Variant: 20

Long-Term Endocrine Sovereignty Anchor

Deep reinforcement of stable internal balance baseline.

01-07 Recovery & Repair Acceleration

Domain 01 — Biological Systems

Focus:
- Recovery pacing
- Repair capacity support
- Post-strain stabilization
- Tissue recovery orientation
- Baseline restoration

Entry 1

Structural Code: **107120114**
Catalog ID: CRP-01-07-0001
Function: Stabilize (1)
Intensity: Class II
Variant: 01

Recovery Stability Anchor

Stabilizes recovery rhythm after strain.

Entry 2

Structural Code: **107220127**
Function: Increase (2)

Intensity: Class II
Variant: 02

Repair Capacity Increase

Supports stronger recovery availability.

Entry 3

Structural Code: **107320135**
Function: Decrease (3)
Intensity: Class I
Variant: 03

Recovery Delay Reduction

Reduces prolonged post-load sluggishness.

Entry 4

Structural Code: **107420146**
Function: Repair (4)
Intensity: Class II
Variant: 04

Repair Cycle Reset

Supports restoration after disruption.

Entry 5

Structural Code: **107520153**
Function: Protect (5)
Intensity: Class II
Variant: 05

Recovery Protection Shield

Protects recovery capacity during ongoing demand.

Entry 6

Structural Code: **107620169**
Function: Amplify (6)
Intensity: Class II
Variant: 06

Regeneration Amplifier

Strengthens repair-oriented recovery state.

Entry 7

Structural Code: **107720176**
Function: Recalibrate (7)
Intensity: Class I
Variant: 07

Load-to-Recovery Calibration

Aligns effort output with realistic recovery needs.

Entry 8

Structural Code: **107820188**
Function: Accelerate (8)
Intensity: Class I
Variant: 08

Recovery Acceleration

Improves speed of return toward baseline.

Entry 9

Structural Code: **107220194**
Function: Increase (2)
Intensity: Class III
Variant: 09

High-Resilience Recovery Surge

Advanced reinforcement of rapid restoration capacity.

Entry 10

Structural Code: **107320203**
Function: Decrease (3)

Intensity: Class II
Variant: 10

Strain Sensitivity Reduction

Reduces overreaction to physical load.

Entry 11

Structural Code: **107520214**
Function: Protect (5)
Intensity: Class III
Variant: 11

Repair Integrity Lock

Deep protection of recovery systems under stress.

Entry 12

Structural Code: **107620227**
Function: Amplify (6)
Intensity: Class II
Variant: 12

Restorative Efficiency Amplifier

Improves quality of recovery periods.

Entry 13

Structural Code: **107420236**
Function: Repair (4)
Intensity: Class I
Variant: 13

Overload Recovery Reset

Supports stabilization after overexertion.

Entry 14

Structural Code: **107720245**
Function: Recalibrate (7)
Intensity: Class II
Variant: 14

Recovery Priority Calibration

Aligns daily behavior toward repair first.

Entry 15

Structural Code: **107120254**
Function: Stabilize (1)
Intensity: Class I
Variant: 15

Rest Rhythm Stability Anchor

Reinforces consistent rest scheduling.

Entry 16

Structural Code: **107820263**
Function: Accelerate (8)
Intensity: Class II
Variant: 16

Repair Momentum Boost

Encourages forward recovery progression.

Entry 17

Structural Code: **107220272**
Function: Increase (2)
Intensity: Class II
Variant: 17

Resilience Capacity Increase

Supports stronger baseline durability.

Entry 18

Structural Code: **107320281**
Function: Decrease (3)

Intensity: Class II
Variant: 18

Inflammation-After-Load Reduction

Reduces reactive post-strain response patterns.

Entry 19

Structural Code: **107620296**
Function: Amplify (6)
Intensity: Class I
Variant: 19

Recovery Discipline Reinforcement

Strengthens consistent recovery habits.

Entry 20

Structural Code: **107520305**
Function: Protect (5)
Intensity: Class III
Variant: 20

Long-Term Recovery Sovereignty Anchor

Deep reinforcement of durable repair baseline.

1-08 Immune System Reinforcement

Domain 01 — Biological Systems

Focus:
- Immune resilience support
- Recovery pacing
- Adaptive response stability
- Baseline protection
- Overload containment

Entry 1

Structural Code: **108120114**
Catalog ID: CRP-01-08-0001
Function: Stabilize (1)
Intensity: Class II
Variant: 01

Immune Stability Anchor

Supports stable immune response behavior.

Entry 2

Structural Code: **108220127**
Function: Increase (2)

Intensity: Class II
Variant: 02

Immune Resilience Increase

Supports stronger adaptive response capacity.

Entry 3

Structural Code: **108320135**
Function: Decrease (3)
Intensity: Class I
Variant: 03

Immune Overreaction Reduction

Reduces excessive reactivity patterns.

Entry 4

Structural Code: **108420146**
Function: Repair (4)
Intensity: Class II
Variant: 04

Post-Illness Recovery Reset

Supports restoration after immune strain.

Entry 5

Structural Code: **108520153**
Function: Protect (5)
Intensity: Class II
Variant: 05

Immune Protection Shield

Protects baseline resilience under exposure pressure.

Entry 6

Structural Code: **108620169**
Function: Amplify (6)
Intensity: Class II
Variant: 06

Adaptive Response Amplifier

Strengthens immune response efficiency.

Entry 7

Structural Code: **108720176**
Function: Recalibrate (7)
Intensity: Class I
Variant: 07

Reactivity Threshold Calibration

Aligns response intensity toward stability.

Entry 8

Structural Code: **108820188**
Function: Accelerate (8)
Intensity: Class I
Variant: 08

Recovery Acceleration (Immune)

Improves speed of return to baseline after strain.

Entry 9

Structural Code: **108220194**
Function: Increase (2)
Intensity: Class III
Variant: 09

High-Resilience Immune Surge

Advanced reinforcement of durable immune stability.

Entry 10

Structural Code: **108320203**
Function: Decrease (3)
Intensity: Class II
Variant: 10

Exposure Sensitivity Reduction

Reduces destabilization during environmental load.

Entry 11

Structural Code: **108520214**
Function: Protect (5)
Intensity: Class III
Variant: 11

Immune Integrity Lock

Deep protection of baseline immune resilience.

Entry 12

Structural Code: **108620227**
Function: Amplify (6)
Intensity: Class II
Variant: 12

Recovery Efficiency Amplifier (Immune)

Strengthens rebound pacing after exposure.

Entry 13

Structural Code: **108420236**
Function: Repair (4)
Intensity: Class I
Variant: 13

Immune Fatigue Recovery

Supports stabilization after repeated immune stress.

Entry 14

Structural Code: **108720245**
Function: Recalibrate (7)
Intensity: Class II
Variant: 14

Adaptive Balance Calibration

Aligns immune response toward efficient stability.

Entry 15

Structural Code: **108120254**
Function: Stabilize (1)
Intensity: Class I
Variant: 15

Daily Resilience Anchor

Reinforces consistent immune-supporting rhythm.

Entry 16

Structural Code: **108820263**
Function: Accelerate (8)
Intensity: Class II
Variant: 16

Immune Recovery Speed Boost

Improves restoration after strain periods.

Entry 17

Structural Code: **108220272**
Function: Increase (2)
Intensity: Class II
Variant: 17

Baseline Resilience Increase

Supports stronger long-term stability.

Entry 18

Structural Code: **108320281**
Function: Decrease (3)
Intensity: Class II
Variant: 18

Inflammatory Immune Noise Reduction

Reduces persistent reactivity background patterns.

Entry 19

Structural Code: **108620296**
Function: Amplify (6)
Intensity: Class I
Variant: 19

Resilience Habit Reinforcement

Strengthens consistent immune stability habits.

Entry 20

Structural Code: **108520305**
Function: Protect (5)
Intensity: Class III
Variant: 20

Immune Sovereignty Anchor

Deep reinforcement of durable immune stability baseline.

01-09 Digestive Regulation

Domain 01 — Biological Systems

Focus:
- Gut stability support
- Stress–digestion interaction regulation
- Motility rhythm stabilization
- Absorption orientation support
- Sensitivity reduction
- Recovery pacing

Entry 1

Structural Code: **109120114**
Catalog ID: CRP-01-09-0001
Function: Stabilize (1)
Intensity: Class II
Variant: 01

Digestive Rhythm Stability Anchor

Supports stable digestive pacing and routine.

Entry 2

Structural Code: **109220127**
Function: Increase (2)

Intensity: Class II
Variant: 02

Digestive Resilience Increase

Supports steadier digestive tolerance under load.

Entry 3

Structural Code: **109320135**
Function: Decrease (3)
Intensity: Class I
Variant: 03

Digestive Sensitivity Reduction

Reduces reactivity patterns to daily inputs.

Entry 4

Structural Code: **109420146**
Function: Repair (4)
Intensity: Class II
Variant: 04

Digestive Disruption Recovery Reset

Supports stabilization after irregular cycles.

Entry 5

Structural Code: **109520153**
Function: Protect (5)
Intensity: Class II
Variant: 05

Gut Stability Protection Shield

Protects baseline digestive steadiness during stress.

Entry 6

Structural Code: **109620169**
Function: Amplify (6)
Intensity: Class II
Variant: 06

Absorption Orientation Amplifier

Strengthens consistency of nutrient-processing focus.

Entry 7

Structural Code: **109720176**
Function: Recalibrate (7)

Intensity: Class I
Variant: 07

Stress–Digestion Calibration

Aligns digestion state with calmer baseline regulation.

Entry 8

Structural Code: **109820188**
Function: Accelerate (8)
Intensity: Class I
Variant: 08

Digestive Recovery Acceleration

Improves speed of return to digestive stability.

Entry 9

Structural Code: **109220194**
Function: Increase (2)
Intensity: Class III
Variant: 09

High-Resilience Digestive Surge

Advanced reinforcement of durable digestive stability.

Entry 10

Structural Code: **109320203**
Function: Decrease (3)
Intensity: Class II
Variant: 10

Bloating/Load Sensitivity Reduction

Reduces discomfort-pattern reinforcement under load.

Entry 11

Structural Code: **109520214**
Function: Protect (5)
Intensity: Class III
Variant: 11

Digestive Integrity Lock

Deep protection of baseline digestive steadiness.

Entry 12

Structural Code: **109620227**
Function: Amplify (6)
Intensity: Class II
Variant: 12

Motility Rhythm Amplifier

Supports consistent digestive movement timing.

Entry 13

Structural Code: **109420236**
Function: Repair (4)
Intensity: Class I
Variant: 13

Irregularity Recovery Reset

Supports stabilization after disrupted rhythm.

Entry 14

Structural Code: **109720245**
Function: Recalibrate (7)
Intensity: Class II
Variant: 14

Appetite–Digestion Calibration

Aligns intake cues with stable digestion pacing.

Entry 15

Structural Code: **109120254**
Function: Stabilize (1)
Intensity: Class I
Variant: 15

Meal Rhythm Stability Anchor

Reinforces consistent meal timing and digestion routine.

Entry 16

Structural Code: **109820263**
Function: Accelerate (8)
Intensity: Class II
Variant: 16

Digestive Stability Speed Boost

Improves rebound after stress-related disruption.

Entry 17

Structural Code: **109220272**
Function: Increase (2)
Intensity: Class II
Variant: 17

Tolerance Capacity Increase

Supports steadier response to normal variability.

Entry 18

Structural Code: **109320281**
Function: Decrease (3)
Intensity: Class II
Variant: 18

Stress-Linked Digestive Noise Reduction

Reduces background stress interference with digestion.

Entry 19

Structural Code: **109620296**
Function: Amplify (6)
Intensity: Class I
Variant: 19

Digestive Discipline Reinforcement

Strengthens consistent regulation habits.

Entry 20

Structural Code: **109520305**
Function: Protect (5)
Intensity: Class III
Variant: 20

Digestive Sovereignty Anchor

Deep reinforcement of long-term digestive stability baseline.

01-10 Cardiovascular Stability

Domain 01 — Biological Systems

Focus:
- Circulatory stability support
- Stress–cardio interaction regulation
- Rhythm steadiness
- Load tolerance support
- Baseline resilience

Entry 1

Structural Code: **110120114**
Catalog ID: CRP-01-10-0001
Function: Stabilize (1)
Intensity: Class II
Variant: 01

Cardiovascular Rhythm Stability Anchor

Supports stable cardiovascular pacing under normal load.

Entry 2

Structural Code: **110220127**
Function: Increase (2)

Intensity: Class II
Variant: 02

Circulatory Resilience Increase

Supports steadier load tolerance.

Entry 3

Structural Code: **110320135**
Function: Decrease (3)
Intensity: Class I
Variant: 03

Stress-Driven Cardio Reactivity Reduction

Reduces overactivation patterns linked to stress.

Entry 4

Structural Code: **110420146**
Function: Repair (4)
Intensity: Class II
Variant: 04

Recovery Rhythm Reset (Cardio)

Supports stabilization after strain or disruption.

Entry 5

Structural Code: **110520153**
Function: Protect (5)
Intensity: Class II
Variant: 05

Cardiovascular Stability Protection Shield

Protects baseline steadiness during pressure periods.

Entry 6

Structural Code: **110620169**
Function: Amplify (6)
Intensity: Class II
Variant: 06

Circulatory Efficiency Amplifier

Supports steadier output with less perceived strain.

Entry 7

Structural Code: **110720176**
Function: Recalibrate (7)
Intensity: Class I
Variant: 07

Load Perception Calibration

Aligns perceived exertion with actual capacity.

Entry 8

Structural Code: **110820188**
Function: Accelerate (8)
Intensity: Class I
Variant: 08

Recovery Downshift Acceleration (Cardio)

Improves speed of return toward calm rhythm.

Entry 9

Structural Code: **110220194**
Function: Increase (2)
Intensity: Class III
Variant: 09

High-Resilience Circulatory Surge

Advanced reinforcement of durable cardiovascular steadiness.

Entry 10

Structural Code: **110320203**
Function: Decrease (3)
Intensity: Class II
Variant: 10

Palpitation Sensitivity Reduction

Reduces reactivity and attention-lock on rhythm fluctuations.

Entry 11

Structural Code: **110520214**
Function: Protect (5)
Intensity: Class III
Variant: 11

Cardiovascular Integrity Lock

Deep protection of stable baseline pacing.

Entry 12

Structural Code: **110620227**
Function: Amplify (6)
Intensity: Class II
Variant: 12

Recovery Efficiency Amplifier (Cardio)

Supports smoother recovery after exertion.

Entry 13

Structural Code: **110420236**
Function: Repair (4)
Intensity: Class I
Variant: 13

Strain Recovery Reset

Supports stabilization after overload episodes.

Entry 14

Structural Code: **110720245**
Function: Recalibrate (7)

Intensity: Class II
Variant: 14

Rhythm Stability Calibration

Aligns pacing toward consistent baseline.

Entry 15

Structural Code: **110120254**
Function: Stabilize (1)
Intensity: Class I
Variant: 15

Daily Cardio Stability Anchor

Reinforces steady daily rhythm orientation.

Entry 16

Structural Code: **110820263**
Function: Accelerate (8)
Intensity: Class II
Variant: 16

Recovery Speed Boost (Cardio)

Improves return-to-baseline speed after stress or effort.

Entry 17

Structural Code: **110220272**
Function: Increase (2)
Intensity: Class II
Variant: 17

Endurance Capacity Increase

Supports more stable sustained effort.

Entry 18

Structural Code: **110320281**
Function: Decrease (3)
Intensity: Class II
Variant: 18

Blood Pressure Reactivity Reduction

Supports steadier response under pressure conditions.

Entry 19

Structural Code: **110620296**
Function: Amplify (6)
Intensity: Class I
Variant: 19

Baseline Resilience Reinforcement (Cardio)

Strengthens consistent steadiness habits.

Entry 20

Structural Code: **110520305**
Function: Protect (5)
Intensity: Class III
Variant: 20

Cardiovascular Sovereignty Anchor

Deep reinforcement of long-term cardiovascular stability baseline.

01-11 Pain Signal Modulation

Domain 01 — Biological Systems

Focus:
- Pain sensitivity reduction support
- Tension pattern release
- Signal amplification control
- Recovery pacing
- Baseline steadiness

Entry 1

Structural Code: **111120114**
Catalog ID: CRP-01-11-0001
Function: Stabilize (1)
Intensity: Class II
Variant: 01

Pain Signal Stability Anchor

Supports steadier pain signal perception and baseline calm.

Entry 2

Structural Code: **111220127**
Function: Increase (2)
Intensity: Class II
Variant: 02

Comfort Baseline Increase

Supports improved comfort-state availability.

Entry 3

Structural Code: **111320135**
Function: Decrease (3)
Intensity: Class I
Variant: 03

Pain Sensitivity Reduction

Reduces sensitivity patterns and amplification loops.

Entry 4

Structural Code: **111420146**
Function: Repair (4)
Intensity: Class II
Variant: 04

Pain Loop Recovery Reset

Supports reset after flare cycles.

Entry 5

Structural Code: **111520153**
Function: Protect (5)
Intensity: Class II
Variant: 05

Comfort Protection Shield

Protects baseline comfort during stress load.

Entry 6

Structural Code: **111620169**
Function: Amplify (6)
Intensity: Class II
Variant: 06

Release Capacity Amplifier

Supports tension-release orientation and relaxation.

Entry 7

Structural Code: **111720176**
Function: Recalibrate (7)
Intensity: Class I
Variant: 07

Signal Interpretation Calibration

Aligns perception away from catastrophic amplification.

Entry 8

Structural Code: **111820188**
Function: Accelerate (8)
Intensity: Class I
Variant: 08

Relief Access Acceleration

Improves speed of downshifting discomfort.

Entry 9

Structural Code: **111220194**
Function: Increase (2)
Intensity: Class III
Variant: 09

High-Comfort Stability Surge

Advanced reinforcement of sustained comfort baseline.

Entry 10

Structural Code: **111320203**
Function: Decrease (3)

Intensity: Class II
Variant: 10

Tension Load Reduction

Reduces held tension contributing to discomfort.

Entry 11

Structural Code: **111520214**
Function: Protect (5)
Intensity: Class III
Variant: 11

Pain Sovereignty Lock

Deep protection of stable comfort baseline.

Entry 12

Structural Code: **111620227**
Function: Amplify (6)
Intensity: Class II
Variant: 12

Recovery Calm Amplifier

Strengthens calm-state support during recovery.

Entry 13

Structural Code: **111420236**
Function: Repair (4)
Intensity: Class I
Variant: 13

Flare Recovery Reset

Supports rebound after discomfort spikes.

Entry 14

Structural Code: **111720245**
Function: Recalibrate (7)
Intensity: Class II
Variant: 14

Sensitivity Threshold Calibration

Aligns thresholds toward stability.

Entry 15

Structural Code: **111120254**
Function: Stabilize (1)
Intensity: Class I
Variant: 15

Daily Comfort Stability Anchor

Reinforces steadier daily comfort rhythm.

Entry 16

Structural Code: **111820263**
Function: Accelerate (8)
Intensity: Class II
Variant: 16

Recovery Relief Speed Boost

Improves rebound speed after strain.

Entry 17

Structural Code: **111220272**
Function: Increase (2)
Intensity: Class II
Variant: 17

Resilience-to-Discomfort Increase

Supports steadier functioning under minor discomfort.

Entry 18

Structural Code: **111320281**
Function: Decrease (3)
Intensity: Class II
Variant: 18

Pain Attention Lock Reduction

Reduces obsessive tracking and amplification.

Entry 19

Structural Code: **111620296**
Function: Amplify (6)
Intensity: Class I
Variant: 19

Release Discipline Reinforcement

Strengthens consistent relaxation and recovery habits.

Entry 20

Structural Code: **111520305**
Function: Protect (5)
Intensity: Class III
Variant: 20

Long-Term Comfort Anchor

Deep reinforcement of stable comfort baseline.

01-12 Neuroplasticity Reinforcement

Domain 01 — Biological Systems

Focus:
- Adaptive capacity support
- Learning-state stability
- Habit rewiring orientation
- Cognitive flexibility reinforcement
- Recovery-supported change

Entry 1

Structural Code: **112120114**
Catalog ID: CRP-01-12-0001
Function: Stabilize (1)
Intensity: Class II
Variant: 01

Adaptive Stability Anchor

Supports stable learning-state access and flexibility.

Entry 2

Structural Code: **112220127**
Function: Increase (2)

Intensity: Class II
Variant: 02

Neuroplastic Capacity Increase

Supports stronger adaptability and rewiring orientation.

Entry 3

Structural Code: **112320135**
Function: Decrease (3)
Intensity: Class I
Variant: 03

Rigidity Pattern Reduction

Reduces stuck-state behavior and cognitive resistance.

Entry 4

Structural Code: **112420146**
Function: Repair (4)
Intensity: Class II
Variant: 04

Learning Disruption Recovery Reset

Supports recovery after cognitive overload or setback.

Entry 5

Structural Code: **112520153**
Function: Protect (5)
Intensity: Class II
Variant: 05

Adaptation Protection Shield

Protects progress during stress periods.

Entry 6

Structural Code: **112620169**
Function: Amplify (6)
Intensity: Class II
Variant: 06

Learning Signal Amplifier

Strengthens receptivity and training effectiveness.

Entry 7

Structural Code: **112720176**
Function: Recalibrate (7)
Intensity: Class I
Variant: 07

Habit Rewiring Calibration

Aligns behavior change with realistic pacing.

Entry 8

Structural Code: **112820188**
Function: Accelerate (8)
Intensity: Class I
Variant: 08

Adaptation Acceleration

Improves speed of integrating new patterns.

Entry 9

Structural Code: **112220194**
Function: Increase (2)
Intensity: Class III
Variant: 09

High-Plasticity Surge

Advanced reinforcement of strong adaptive change capacity.

Entry 10

Structural Code: **112320203**
Function: Decrease (3)
Intensity: Class II
Variant: 10

Cognitive Fatigue Interference Reduction

Reduces fatigue-related resistance to learning.

Entry 11

Structural Code: **112520214**
Function: Protect (5)
Intensity: Class III
Variant: 11

Neuroplastic Integrity Lock

Deep protection of adaptation capacity under strain.

Entry 12

Structural Code: **112620227**
Function: Amplify (6)
Intensity: Class II
Variant: 12

Training Efficiency Amplifier

Strengthens learning yield per effort.

Entry 13

Structural Code: **112420236**
Function: Repair (4)
Intensity: Class I
Variant: 13

Setback Recovery Reset (Learning)

Supports resilience after relapse or interruption.

Entry 14

Structural Code: **112720245**
Function: Recalibrate (7)
Intensity: Class II
Variant: 14

Flexibility Threshold Calibration

Aligns responsiveness without instability.

Entry 15

Structural Code: **112120254**
Function: Stabilize (1)
Intensity: Class I
Variant: 15

Consistent Growth Anchor

Reinforces steady learning rhythm.

Entry 16

Structural Code: **112820263**
Function: Accelerate (8)
Intensity: Class II
Variant: 16

Habit Integration Speed Boost

Improves consolidation of new behavior.

Entry 17

Structural Code: **112220272**
Function: Increase (2)
Intensity: Class II
Variant: 17

Cognitive Flexibility Increase

Supports adaptive thinking and switching ability.

Entry 18

Structural Code: **112320281**
Function: Decrease (3)
Intensity: Class II
Variant: 18

Self-Sabotage Loop Reduction

Reduces automatic relapse patterns during change.

Entry 19

Structural Code: **112620296**
Function: Amplify (6)
Intensity: Class I
Variant: 19

Adaptive Discipline Reinforcement

Strengthens consistent practice habits.

Entry 20

Structural Code: **112520305**
Function: Protect (5)

Intensity: Class III
Variant: 20

Long-Term Adaptation Sovereignty Anchor

Deep reinforcement of durable neuroplastic stability.

01-13 Sensory Processing Calibration

Domain 01 — Biological Systems

Focus:
- Overstimulation reduction
- Noise/light sensitivity calibration
- Sensory gating stability
- Input tolerance support
- Recovery after overload

Entry 1

Structural Code: **113120114**
Catalog ID: CRP-01-13-0001
Function: Stabilize (1)
Intensity: Class II
Variant: 01

Sensory Gating Stability Anchor

Supports stable filtering of sensory input.

Entry 2

Structural Code: **113220127**
Function: Increase (2)
Intensity: Class II
Variant: 02

Input Tolerance Increase

Supports steadier tolerance to normal sensory load.

Entry 3

Structural Code: **113320135**
Function: Decrease (3)
Intensity: Class I
Variant: 03

Overstimulation Reduction

Reduces overload response to sensory intensity.

Entry 4

Structural Code: **113420146**
Function: Repair (4)
Intensity: Class II
Variant: 04

Overload Recovery Reset

Supports recovery after sensory saturation.

Entry 5

Structural Code: **113520153**
Function: Protect (5)
Intensity: Class II
Variant: 05

Sensory Stability Protection Shield

Protects regulation during high-input environments.

Entry 6

Structural Code: **113620169**
Function: Amplify (6)
Intensity: Class II
Variant: 06

Regulation Filter Amplifier

Strengthens sensory filtering efficiency.

Entry 7

Structural Code: **113720176**
Function: Recalibrate (7)

Intensity: Class I
Variant: 07

Sensitivity Threshold Calibration

Aligns sensitivity toward stable tolerance.

Entry 8

Structural Code: **113820188**
Function: Accelerate (8)
Intensity: Class I
Variant: 08

Downshift Acceleration (Sensory)

Improves speed of calming after sensory overload.

Entry 9

Structural Code: **113220194**
Function: Increase (2)
Intensity: Class III
Variant: 09

High-Tolerance Sensory Surge

Advanced reinforcement of stable input tolerance.

Entry 10

Structural Code: **113320203**
Function: Decrease (3)
Intensity: Class II
Variant: 10

Noise Sensitivity Reduction

Reduces reactivity to auditory load.

Entry 11

Structural Code: **113520214**
Function: Protect (5)
Intensity: Class III
Variant: 11

Sensory Integrity Lock

Deep protection of stable sensory gating.

Entry 12

Structural Code: **113620227**
Function: Amplify (6)

Intensity: Class II
Variant: 12

Calm Filter Amplifier

Strengthens regulated filtering during daily input.

Entry 13

Structural Code: **113420236**
Function: Repair (4)
Intensity: Class I
Variant: 13

Light Sensitivity Recovery Reset

Supports stabilization after visual overload.

Entry 14

Structural Code: **113720245**
Function: Recalibrate (7)
Intensity: Class II
Variant: 14

Environmental Load Calibration

Aligns response to real environmental intensity.

Entry 15

Structural Code: **113120254**
Function: Stabilize (1)
Intensity: Class I
Variant: 15

Daily Input Stability Anchor

Reinforces stable tolerance throughout day.

Entry 16

Structural Code: **113820263**
Function: Accelerate (8)
Intensity: Class II
Variant: 16

Overstimulation Recovery Speed Boost

Improves rebound after overload events.

Entry 17

Structural Code: **113220272**
Function: Increase (2)

Intensity: Class II
Variant: 17

Sensory Resilience Increase

Supports steadier regulation under high input.

Entry 18

Structural Code: **113320281**
Function: Decrease (3)
Intensity: Class II
Variant: 18

Crowded-Environment Reactivity Reduction

Reduces overload in busy settings.

Entry 19

Structural Code: **113620296**
Function: Amplify (6)
Intensity: Class I
Variant: 19

Sensory Discipline Reinforcement

Strengthens consistent boundary and recovery habits.

Entry 20

Structural Code: **113520305**
Function: Protect (5)
Intensity: Class III
Variant: 20

Long-Term Sensory Sovereignty Anchor

Deep reinforcement of durable sensory stability baseline.

01-14 Breath & Autonomic Regulation

Domain 01 — Biological Systems

Focus:
- Breath rhythm stability
- Downshift control
- CO_2 tolerance orientation
- Calm-state induction
- Autonomic reset anchors
- Panic-loop interruption support

Entry 1

Structural Code: **114120114**
Catalog ID: CRP-01-14-0001
Function: Stabilize (1)
Intensity: Class II
Variant: 01

Breath Rhythm Stability Anchor

Stabilizes breathing pace and baseline rhythm.

Entry 2

Structural Code: **114220127**
Function: Increase (2)
Intensity: Class II
Variant: 02

CO_2 Tolerance Capacity Increase

Supports steadier breathing under stress load.

Entry 3

Structural Code: **114320135**
Function: Decrease (3)
Intensity: Class I
Variant: 03

Breath Holding Tension Reduction

Reduces unconscious breath restriction patterns.

Entry 4

Structural Code: **114420146**
Function: Repair (4)
Intensity: Class II
Variant: 04

Breathing Disruption Recovery Reset

Supports stabilization after dysregulated episodes.

Entry 5

Structural Code: **114520153**
Function: Protect (5)
Intensity: Class II
Variant: 05

Breath Stability Protection Shield

Protects calm breathing rhythm during stress.

Entry 6

Structural Code: **114620169**
Function: Amplify (6)
Intensity: Class II
Variant: 06

Downshift Efficiency Amplifier

Strengthens ability to slow and deepen breath.

Entry 7

Structural Code: **114720176**
Function: Recalibrate (7)
Intensity: Class I
Variant: 07

Panic Threshold Calibration

Aligns response away from runaway escalation.

Entry 8

Structural Code: **114820188**
Function: Accelerate (8)
Intensity: Class I
Variant: 08

Calm Induction Acceleration

Improves speed of shifting into regulated breathing.

Entry 9

Structural Code: **114220194**
Function: Increase (2)
Intensity: Class III
Variant: 09

High-Stability Breath Surge

Advanced reinforcement of deep calm breathing access.

Entry 10

Structural Code: **114320203**
Function: Decrease (3)
Intensity: Class II
Variant: 10

Air Hunger Reactivity Reduction

Reduces panic-linked breathing urgency patterns.

Entry 11

Structural Code: **114520214**
Function: Protect (5)
Intensity: Class III
Variant: 11

Autonomic Breath Integrity Lock

Deep protection of stable autonomic breathing baseline.

Entry 12

Structural Code: **114620227**
Function: Amplify (6)
Intensity: Class II
Variant: 12

Exhale Dominance Amplifier

Strengthens exhale-led downshift capacity.

Entry 13

Structural Code: **114420236**
Function: Repair (4)
Intensity: Class I
Variant: 13

Panic Episode Recovery Reset

Supports return to baseline after spikes.

Entry 14

Structural Code: **114720245**
Function: Recalibrate (7)
Intensity: Class II
Variant: 14

Breath–Emotion Calibration

Aligns emotional response with breath control.

Entry 15

Structural Code: **114120254**
Function: Stabilize (1)
Intensity: Class I
Variant: 15

Daily Breath Discipline Anchor

Reinforces consistent breath regulation practice.

Entry 16

Structural Code: **114820263**
Function: Accelerate (8)
Intensity: Class II
Variant: 16

Downshift Speed Boost

Improves recovery speed after stress surges.

Entry 17

Structural Code: **114220272**
Function: Increase (2)
Intensity: Class II
Variant: 17

Calm Capacity Increase

Supports longer duration calm-state maintenance.

Entry 18

Structural Code: **114320281**
Function: Decrease (3)
Intensity: Class II
Variant: 18

Breathing Pattern Noise Reduction

Reduces erratic breath variability under pressure.

Entry 19

Structural Code: **114620296**
Function: Amplify (6)
Intensity: Class I
Variant: 19

Regulation Habit Reinforcement (Breath)

Strengthens consistent breath-based regulation.

Entry 20

Structural Code: **114520305**
Function: Protect (5)
Intensity: Class III
Variant: 20

Breath Sovereignty Anchor

Deep reinforcement of long-term breath-regulation baseline.

01-15 Biological Baseline Reset

Domain 01 — Biological Systems

Focus:
- Multi-system stabilization
- Overload reduction
- Baseline restoration
- Recovery foundation
- Capacity reset anchors
- Long-term resilience

Entry 1

Structural Code: **115120114**
Catalog ID: CRP-01-15-0001
Function: Stabilize (1)
Intensity: Class II
Variant: 01

Baseline Restoration Anchor

Supports return to stable biological baseline.

Entry 2

Structural Code: **115220127**
Function: Increase (2)
Intensity: Class II
Variant: 02

Recovery Capacity Increase

Supports stronger restoration availability.

Entry 3

Structural Code: **115320135**
Function: Decrease (3)
Intensity: Class I
Variant: 03

Overload Load Reduction

Reduces accumulated strain patterns.

Entry 4

Structural Code: **115420146**
Function: Repair (4)
Intensity: Class II
Variant: 04

System Reset Recovery

Supports re-stabilization after prolonged disruption.

Entry 5

Structural Code: **115520153**
Function: Protect (5)
Intensity: Class II
Variant: 05

Baseline Protection Shield

Protects stability during high-demand periods.

Entry 6

Structural Code: **115620169**
Function: Amplify (6)
Intensity: Class II
Variant: 06

Resilience Amplifier

Strengthens durable baseline stability.

Entry 7

Structural Code: **115720176**
Function: Recalibrate (7)
Intensity: Class I
Variant: 07

Capacity Threshold Calibration

Aligns daily demand with biological capacity.

Entry 8

Structural Code: **115820188**
Function: Accelerate (8)
Intensity: Class I
Variant: 08

Baseline Reset Acceleration

Improves speed of returning to steadier baseline.

Entry 9

Structural Code: **115220194**
Function: Increase (2)
Intensity: Class III
Variant: 09

High-Resilience Baseline Surge

Advanced reinforcement of deep system stability.

Entry 10

Structural Code: **115320203**
Function: Decrease (3)
Intensity: Class II
Variant: 10

Strain Noise Reduction

Reduces ongoing low-grade strain interference.

Entry 11

Structural Code: **115520214**
Function: Protect (5)
Intensity: Class III
Variant: 11

Baseline Integrity Lock

Deep protection of long-term stability foundation.

Entry 12

Structural Code: **115620227**
Function: Amplify (6)
Intensity: Class II
Variant: 12

System Recovery Amplifier

Strengthens recovery efficiency across systems.

Entry 13

Structural Code: **115420236**
Function: Repair (4)
Intensity: Class I
Variant: 13

Collapse Recovery Reset

Supports stabilization after sustained overload.

Entry 14

Structural Code: **115720245**
Function: Recalibrate (7)
Intensity: Class II
Variant: 14

Biological Priority Calibration

Aligns behavior toward restoration-first structure.

Entry 15

Structural Code: **115120254**
Function: Stabilize (1)
Intensity: Class I
Variant: 15

Daily Baseline Stability Anchor

Reinforces consistent foundational stability habits.

Entry 16

Structural Code: **115820263**
Function: Accelerate (8)
Intensity: Class II
Variant: 16

Recovery Cycle Speed Boost

Improves rebound after heavy stress windows.

Entry 17

Structural Code: **115220272**
Function: Increase (2)
Intensity: Class II
Variant: 17

Stability Capacity Increase

Supports holding stable baseline longer.

Entry 18

Structural Code: **115320281**
Function: Decrease (3)
Intensity: Class II
Variant: 18

Fragility Pattern Reduction

Reduces sensitivity to minor stressors.

Entry 19

Structural Code: **115620296**
Function: Amplify (6)
Intensity: Class I
Variant: 19

Resilience Discipline Reinforcement

Strengthens consistent baseline maintenance habits.

Entry 20

Structural Code: **115520305**
Function: Protect (5)
Intensity: Class III
Variant: 20

Biological Sovereignty Anchor

Deep reinforcement of durable, stable baseline foundation.

PART II — INDEX ARCHITECTURE

Domain Index

Domain 01 — Biological & Nervous System

01-01 Nervous System Regulation
01-02 Sleep Architecture Optimization
01-03 Stress Hormone Stabilization
01-04 Inflammatory Response Regulation
01-05 Energy Metabolism Optimization
01-06 Hormonal Structuring
01-07 Recovery & Repair Acceleration
01-08 Immune System Reinforcement
01-09 Digestive Regulation
01-10 Cardiovascular Stability
01-11 Pain Signal Modulation
01-12 Neuroplasticity Reinforcement
01-13 Sensory Processing Calibration
01-14 Breath & Autonomic Regulation
01-15 Biological Baseline Reset

Subsystem Index

01-01 Nervous System Regulation — Entries 0001–0020
01-02 Sleep Architecture Optimization — Entries 0021–0040
01-03 Stress Hormone Stabilization — Entries 0041–0060
01-04 Inflammatory Response Regulation — Entries 0061–0080
01-05 Energy Metabolism Optimization — Entries 0081–0100
01-06 Hormonal Structuring — Entries 0101–0120
01-07 Recovery & Repair Acceleration — Entries 0121–0140
01-08 Immune System Reinforcement — Entries 0141–0160

Functional Index

Function 1 — Stabilize

101120114 101120254 102120114 102120254 103120114
103120254 104120114 104120254 105120114 105120254
106120114 106120254 107120114 107120254 108120114
108120254 109120114 109120254 110120114 110120254
111120114 111120254 112120114 112120254 113120114
113120254 114120114 114120254 115120114 115120254

Function 2 — Increase

101220127 101220194 101220272 102220127 102220194
102220272 103220127 103220194 103220272 104220127
104220194 104220272 105220127 105220194 105220272
106220127 106220194 106220272 107220127 107220194
107220272 108220127 108220194 108220272 109220127
109220194 109220272 110220127 110220194 110220272
111220127 111220194 111220272 112220127 112220194
112220272 113220127 113220194 113220272 114220127
114220194 114220272 115220127 115220194 115220272

Function 3 — Decrease

101320135 101320203 101320281 102320135 102320203
102320281 103320135 103320203 103320281 104320135
104320203 104320281 105320135 105320203 105320281
106320135 106320203 106320281 107320135 107320203
107320281 108320135 108320203 108320281 109320135
109320203 109320281 110320135 110320203 110320281
111320135 111320203 111320281 112320135 112320203
112320281 113320135 113320203 113320281 114320135
114320203 114320281 115320135 115320203 115320281

Function 4 — Repair

101420146 101420236 102420146 102420236 103420146
103420236 104420146 104420236 105420146 105420236
106420146 106420236 107420146 107420236 108420146
108420236 109420146 109420236 110420146 110420236
111420146 111420236 112420146 112420236 113420146
113420236 114420146 114420236 115420146 115420236

Function 5 — Protect

101520153 101520214 101520305 102520153 102520214
102520305 103520153 103520214 103520305 104520153
104520214 104520305 105520153 105520214 105520305
106520153 106520214 106520305 107520153 107520214
107520305 108520153 108520214 108520305 109520153
109520214 109520305 110520153 110520214 110520305
111520153 111520214 111520305 112520153 112520214
112520305 113520153 113520214 113520305 114520153
114520214 114520305 115520153 115520214 115520305

Function 6 — Amplify

101620169 101620227 101620296 102620169 102620227
102620296 103620169 103620227 103620296 104620169
104620227 104620296 105620169 105620227 105620296
106620169 106620227 106620296 107620169 107620227
107620296 108620169 108620227 108620296 109620169

109620227 109620296 110620169 110620227 110620296
111620169 111620227 111620296 112620169 112620227
112620296 113620169 113620227 113620296 114620169
114620227 114620296 115620169 115620227 115620296

Function 7 — Recalibrate

101720176 101720245 102720176 102720245 103720176
103720245 104720176 104720245 105720176 105720245
106720176 106720245 107720176 107720245 108720176
108720245 109720176 109720245 110720176 110720245
111720176 111720245 112720176 112720245 113720176
113720245 114720176 114720245 115720176 115720245

Function 8 — Accelerate

101820188 101820263 102820188 102820263 103820188
103820263 104820188 104820263 105820188 105820263
106820188 106820263 107820188 107820263 108820188
108820263 109820188 109820263 110820188 110820263
111820188 111820263 112820188 112820263 113820188
113820263 114820188 114820263 115820188 115820263

Intensity Index

Class I — Gentle Calibration

101320135 101720176 101820188 101420236 101120254
101620296 102320135 102720176 102820188 102420236
102120254 102620296 103320135 103720176 103820188
103420236 103120254 103620296 104320135 104720176
104820188 104420236 104120254 104620296 105320135
105720176 105820188 105420236 105120254 105620296
106320135 106720176 106820188 106420236 106120254
106620296 107320135 107720176 107820188 107420236
107120254 107620296 108320135 108720176 108820188
108420236 108120254 108620296 109320135 109720176
109820188 109420236 109120254 109620296 110320135

110720176 110820188 110420236 110120254 110620296
111320135 111720176 111820188 111420236 111120254
111620296 112320135 112720176 112820188 112420236
112120254 112620296 113320135 113720176 113820188
113420236 113120254 113620296 114320135 114720176
114820188 114420236 114120254 114620296 115320135
115720176 115820188 115420236 115120254 115620296

Class II — Standard Structural Activation

101120114 101220127 101420146 101520153 101620169
101720245 101220272 101320281 102120114 102220127
102420146 102520153 102620169 102720245 102220272
102320281 103120114 103220127 103420146 103520153
103620169 103720245 103220272 103320281 104120114
104220127 104420146 104520153 104620169 104720245
104220272 104320281 105120114 105220127 105420146
105520153 105620169 105720245 105220272 105320281
106120114 106220127 106420146 106520153 106620169
106720245 106220272 106320281 107120114 107220127
107420146 107520153 107620169 107720245 107220272
107320281 108120114 108220127 108420146 108520153
108620169 108720245 108220272 108320281 109120114
109220127 109420146 109520153 109620169 109720245
109220272 109320281 110120114 110220127 110420146
110520153 110620169 110720245 110220272 110320281
111120114 111220127 111420146 111520153 111620169
111720245 111220272 111320281 112120114 112220127
112420146 112520153 112620169 112720245 112220272
112320281 113120114 113220127 113420146 113520153
113620169 113720245 113220272 113320281 114120114
114220127 114420146 114520153 114620169 114720245
114220272 114320281 115120114 115220127 115420146
115520153 115620169 115720245 115220272 115320281

Class III — High-Intensity Structural Shift

101220194 101520214 101520305 102220194 102520214
102520305 103220194 103520214 103520305 104220194
104520214 104520305 105220194 105520214 105520305
106220194 106520214 106520305 107220194 107520214
107520305 108220194 108520214 108520305 109220194
109520214 109520305 110220194 110520214 110520305
111220194 111520214 111520305 112220194 112520214
112520305 113220194 113520214 113520305 114220194
114520214 114520305 115220194 115520214 115520305

Thematic Keyword Index

Numerical Code Index

102620296 102720176 102720245 102820188 102820263
103120114 103120254 103220127 103220194 103220272
103320135 103320203 103320281 103420146 103420236
103520153 103520214 103520305 103620169 103620227
103620296 103720176 103720245 103820188 103820263
104120114 104120254 104220127 104220194 104220272
104320135 104320203 104320281 104420146 104420236
104520153 104520214 104520305 104620169 104620227
104620296 104720176 104720245 104820188 104820263
105120114 105120254 105220127 105220194 105220272
105320135 105320203 105320281 105420146 105420236
105520153 105520214 105520305 105620169 105620227
105620296 105720176 105720245 105820188 105820263
106120114 106120254 106220127 106220194 106220272
106320135 106320203 106320281 106420146 106420236
106520153 106520214 106520305 106620169 106620227
106620296 106720176 106720245 106820188 106820263
107120114 107120254 107220127 107220194 107220272
107320135 107320203 107320281 107420146 107420236
107520153 107520214 107520305 107620169 107620227
107620296 107720176 107720245 107820188 107820263
108120114 108120254 108220127 108220194 108220272
108320135 108320203 108320281 108420146 108420236
108520153 108520214 108520305 108620169 108620227
108620296 108720176 108720245 108820188 108820263
109120114 109120254 109220127 109220194 109220272
109320135 109320203 109320281 109420146 109420236
109520153 109520214 109520305 109620169 109620227
109620296 109720176 109720245 109820188 109820263
110120114 110120254 110220127 110220194 110220272
110320135 110320203 110320281 110420146 110420236
110520153 110520214 110520305 110620169 110620227
110620296 110720176 110720245 110820188 110820263
111120114 111120254 111220127 111220194 111220272
111320135 111320203 111320281 111420146 111420236
111520153 111520214 111520305 111620169 111620227
111620296 111720176 111720245 111820188 111820263
112120114 112120254 112220127 112220194 112220272
112320135 112320203 112320281 112420146 112420236

112520153 112520214 112520305 112620169 112620227
112620296 112720176 112720245 112820188 112820263
113120114 113120254 113220127 113220194 113220272
113320135 113320203 113320281 113420146 113420236
113520153 113520214 113520305 113620169 113620227
113620296 113720176 113720245 113820188 113820263
114120114 114120254 114220127 114220194 114220272
114320135 114320203 114320281 114420146 114420236
114520153 114520214 114520305 114620169 114620227
114620296 114720176 114720245 114820188 114820263
115120114 115120254 115220127 115220194 115220272
115320135 115320203 115320281 115420146 115420236
115520153 115520214 115520305 115620169 115620227
115620296 115720176 115720245 115820188 115820263

Structural Density Map

Domain 01 — Biological & Nervous System

Total Subsystems: 15
Total Classified Entries: 300
Entries per Subsystem: 20

Functional Distribution:
Stabilize (1) — 30
Increase (2) — 45
Decrease (3) — 45
Repair (4) — 30
Protect (5) — 45
Amplify (6) — 45
Recalibrate (7) — 30
Accelerate (8) — 30

Intensity Distribution:
Class I — 90
Class II — 165
Class III — 45

APPENDICES

Appendix A — Code Generation Algorithm

CRP Structural Codes™ System

A1. Structural Code Format

Each entry uses a **9-digit structural code**:

D SS F I VVV C

Where:

- **D** = Domain (1 digit)
- **SS** = Subsystem (2 digits)
- **F** = Function (1 digit)
- **I** = Intensity (1 digit)
- **VVV** = Variant (3 digits)
- **C** = Check Digit (1 digit)

This produces:

8-digit base + 1-digit check = 9 digits total

A2. Field Definitions

Domain (D)

- Range: 1–9
- Example: Domain 01 (Biological) is written as **1**
- Example: Domain 05 (Financial) is written as **5**

Subsystem (SS)

- Range: 01–99
- Example: Subsystem 01-02 is written as **02**

Function (F)

- 1 Stabilize
- 2 Increase
- 3 Decrease
- 4 Repair
- 5 Protect
- 6 Amplify
- 7 Recalibrate
- 8 Accelerate

Intensity (I)

- 1 Class I — Gentle Calibration
- 2 Class II — Standard Structural Activation
- 3 Class III — High-Intensity Structural Shift
- 4 Class IV — Reserved

Variant (VVV)

- Range: 001–999
- Standard subsystem allocation uses: **001–020** (padded to three digits)
- Expansion capacity is retained for future growth inside the same subsystem.

Check Digit (C)

- Range: 0–9
- Generated using Appendix B validation logic (Option B).

A3. Generation Steps (Standard)

1. **Select Domain (D)**
   Choose the primary domain category for the entry.
2. **Select Subsystem (SS)**
   Choose the subsystem that defines the context bucket.
3. **Assign Function Type (F)**
   Select the action-class that defines what the sequence is meant to do.
4. **Assign Intensity Class (I)**
   Choose Class I–III (Class IV reserved).
5. **Assign Variant (VVV)**
   Allocate sequentially within the subsystem:
   001, 002, 003 ... 020 (standard reference build)
6. **Generate Check Digit (C)**
   Append a final digit derived from the Option B check-digit algorithm (Appendix B).

Result:
A single 9-digit code that is **classified, indexed, and structurally unique**.

A4. Variant Allocation Rule (Reference Build)

Default allocation per subsystem:

- **001–020** = primary reference layer
- **021–060** = expansion layer (future)
- **061–120** = specialist layer (future)
- **121–200** = high-density layer (future)
- **201–999** = reserved for long-horizon scaling

This keeps the system scalable without breaking the indexing structure.

A5. Catalog ID Generation (Book Indexing)

Catalog ID format:

CRP-01-02-0001

Where:

- First pair = Volume Domain label (01, 05, etc.)
- Second pair = Subsystem number (01–15, etc.)
- Last block = entry number within that subsystem (0001–0020)

This ID is for **book navigation**, while the structural code is for **system integrity**.

A6. Example (Structure Only)

Example code anatomy:

1 02 2 2 012 C

- Domain 1 = Biological

- Subsystem 02 = Sleep Architecture
- Function 2 = Increase
- Intensity 2 = Class II
- Variant 012 = sequence slot
- C = check digit (Appendix B)

A7. Reserved Rules

- **Class IV** is reserved for future advanced volumes.
- **Variant capacity** is intentionally oversized to prevent subsystem exhaustion.
- The system is designed so **new subsystems can be added without disturbing existing code order**.

Appendix B — Check-Digit Validation Logic (Option B)

CRP Structural Codes™ System

B1. Purpose of the Check Digit

The final digit (**C**) is a **validation digit**.

It is used to:

- Reduce accidental transcription errors
- Create internal structural consistency

- Prevent "random-number" appearance
- Support fast integrity checks in print workflows

This is a **reference integrity mechanism**, not a cryptographic system.

B2. Option B Method

VC-20 Validation Cycle (Print-Optimized)

Option B is optimized for:

- Speed (manual + spreadsheet friendly)
- Consistency across large catalogs
- Predictable distribution of final digits
- Stable scaling to thousands of entries

The check digit is generated using a **20-step validation cycle** keyed to the **Variant (VVV)**.

B3. VC-20 Validation Cycle Table

Position → Check Digit

01 → 4
02 → 7
03 → 5
04 → 6
05 → 3
06 → 9
07 → 6
08 → 8
09 → 4
10 → 3

11 → 4
12 → 7
13 → 6
14 → 5
15 → 4
16 → 3
17 → 2
18 → 1
19 → 6
20 → 5

This table is the **Option B standard** for the series.

B4. Generation Steps

Given the 8-digit base:

D SS F I VVV (8 digits)

1. Extract **VVV** (Variant) as an integer **v**
2. Compute cycle position:

$$p = ((v - 1) \bmod 20) + 1$$

3. Look up the check digit:

$$C = VC\text{-}20[p]$$

4. Append **C** to the base to form the 9-digit structural code.

B5. Validation Steps (Integrity Check)

To validate any printed code:

1. Read the code and isolate **VVV**
2. Compute **p** using the formula above
3. Confirm the final digit matches **VC-20[p]**

If it matches, the code passes Option B validation.

B6. Examples

Example 1
Code: **101120114**
Variant **VVV = 011** → v = 11
p = ((11 − 1) mod 20) + 1 = 11
VC-20[11] = **4**
Check digit matches → **VALID**

Example 2
Code: **102220127**
Variant **VVV = 012** → v = 12
p = 12
VC-20[12] = **7**
Check digit matches → **VALID**

B7. Scaling Rule (Beyond 020)

The cycle repeats every 20 variants:

- VVV = 021 maps to Position 01
- VVV = 040 maps to Position 20
- VVV = 041 maps to Position 01 again

This keeps validation stable while allowing high-density subsystems.

VOLUME II — VALIDATED STRUCTURAL CODE LIST (OPTION B)

Format: CRP-01-SS-#### — DSSFIVVVC

01-01 Nervous System Regulation

CRP-01-01-0001 — 101120014

CRP-01-01-0002 — 101220027

CRP-01-01-0003 — 101310035

CRP-01-01-0004 — 101420046

CRP-01-01-0005 — 101520053

CRP-01-01-0006 — 101620069

CRP-01-01-0007 — 101710076

CRP-01-01-0008 — 101810088

CRP-01-01-0009 — 101230094

CRP-01-01-0010 — 101320103

CRP-01-01-0011 — 101530114

CRP-01-01-0012 — 101620127

CRP-01-01-0013 — 101410136

CRP-01-01-0014 — 101720145

CRP-01-01-0015 — 101110154

CRP-01-01-0016 — 101820163

CRP-01-01-0017 — 101220172

CRP-01-01-0018 — 101320181

CRP-01-01-0019 — 101610196

CRP-01-01-0020 — 101530205

01-02 Sleep Architecture Optimization

CRP-01-02-0001 — 102120014

CRP-01-02-0002 — 102220027

CRP-01-02-0003 — 102310035

CRP-01-02-0004 — 102420046

CRP-01-02-0005 — 102520053

CRP-01-02-0006 — 102620069

CRP-01-02-0007 — 102710076

CRP-01-02-0008 — 102810088

CRP-01-02-0009 — 102230094

CRP-01-02-0010 — 102320103

CRP-01-02-0011 — 102530114

CRP-01-02-0012 — 102620127

CRP-01-02-0013 — 102410136

CRP-01-02-0014 — 102720145

CRP-01-02-0015 — 102110154

CRP-01-02-0016 — 102820163

CRP-01-02-0017 — 102220172

CRP-01-02-0018 — 102320181

CRP-01-02-0019 — 102610196

CRP-01-02-0020 — 102530205

01-03 Stress Hormone Stabilization

CRP-01-03-0001 — 103120014

CRP-01-03-0002 — 103220027

CRP-01-03-0003 — 103310035

CRP-01-03-0004 — 103420046

CRP-01-03-0005 — 103520053

CRP-01-03-0006 — 103620069

CRP-01-03-0007 — 103710076

CRP-01-03-0008 — 103810088

CRP-01-03-0009 — 103230094

CRP-01-03-0010 — 103320103

CRP-01-03-0011 — 103530114

CRP-01-03-0012 — 103620127

CRP-01-03-0013 — 103410136

CRP-01-03-0014 — 103720145

CRP-01-03-0015 — 103110154

CRP-01-03-0016 — 103820163

CRP-01-03-0017 — 103220172

CRP-01-03-0018 — 103320181

CRP-01-03-0019 — 103610196

CRP-01-03-0020 — 103530205

01-04 Inflammatory Response Regulation

CRP-01-04-0001 — 104120014

CRP-01-04-0002 — 104220027

CRP-01-04-0003 — 104310035

CRP-01-04-0004 — 104420046

CRP-01-04-0005 — 104520053

CRP-01-04-0006 — 104620069

CRP-01-04-0007 — 104710076

CRP-01-04-0008 — 104810088

CRP-01-04-0009 — 104230094

CRP-01-04-0010 — 104320103

CRP-01-04-0011 — 104530114

CRP-01-04-0012 — 104620127

CRP-01-04-0013 — 104410136

CRP-01-04-0014 — 104720145

CRP-01-04-0015 — 104110154

CRP-01-04-0016 — 104820163

CRP-01-04-0017 — 104220172

CRP-01-04-0018 — 104320181

CRP-01-04-0019 — 104610196

CRP-01-04-0020 — 104530205

01-05 Energy Metabolism Optimization

CRP-01-05-0001 — 105120014

CRP-01-05-0002 — 105220027

CRP-01-05-0003 — 105310035

CRP-01-05-0004 — 105420046

CRP-01-05-0005 — 105520053

CRP-01-05-0006 — 105620069

CRP-01-05-0007 — 105710076

CRP-01-05-0008 — 105810088

CRP-01-05-0009 — 105230094

CRP-01-05-0010 — 105320103

CRP-01-05-0011 — 105530114

CRP-01-05-0012 — 105620127

CRP-01-05-0013 — 105410136

CRP-01-05-0014 — 105720145

CRP-01-05-0015 — 105110154

CRP-01-05-0016 — 105820163

CRP-01-05-0017 — 105220172

CRP-01-05-0018 — 105320181

CRP-01-05-0019 — 105610196

CRP-01-05-0020 — 105530205

01-06 Hormonal Structuring

CRP-01-06-0001 — 106120014

CRP-01-06-0002 — 106220027

CRP-01-06-0003 — 106310035

CRP-01-06-0004 — 106420046

CRP-01-06-0005 — 106520053

CRP-01-06-0006 — 106620069

CRP-01-06-0007 — 106710076

CRP-01-06-0008 — 106810088

CRP-01-06-0009 — 106230094

CRP-01-06-0010 — 106320103

CRP-01-06-0011 — 106530114

CRP-01-06-0012 — 106620127

CRP-01-06-0013 — 106410136

CRP-01-06-0014 — 106720145

CRP-01-06-0015 — 106110154

CRP-01-06-0016 — 106820163

CRP-01-06-0017 — 106220172

CRP-01-06-0018 — 106320181

CRP-01-06-0019 — 106610196

CRP-01-06-0020 — 106530205

01-07 Recovery & Repair Acceleration

CRP-01-07-0001 — 107120014

CRP-01-07-0002 — 107220027

CRP-01-07-0003 — 107310035

CRP-01-07-0004 — 107420046

CRP-01-07-0005 — 107520053

CRP-01-07-0006 — 107620069

CRP-01-07-0007 — 107710076

CRP-01-07-0008 — 107810088

CRP-01-07-0009 — 107230094

CRP-01-07-0010 — 107320103

CRP-01-07-0011 — 107530114

CRP-01-07-0012 — 107620127

CRP-01-07-0013 — 107410136

CRP-01-07-0014 — 107720145

CRP-01-07-0015 — 107110154

CRP-01-07-0016 — 107820163

CRP-01-07-0017 — 107220172

CRP-01-07-0018 — 107320181

CRP-01-07-0019 — 107610196

CRP-01-07-0020 — 107530205

01-08 Immune System Reinforcement

CRP-01-08-0001 — 108120014

CRP-01-08-0002 — 108220027

CRP-01-08-0003 — 108310035

CRP-01-08-0004 — 108420046

CRP-01-08-0005 — 108520053

CRP-01-08-0006 — 108620069

CRP-01-08-0007 — 108710076

CRP-01-08-0008 — 108810088

CRP-01-08-0009 — 108230094

CRP-01-08-0010 — 108320103

CRP-01-08-0011 — 108530114

CRP-01-08-0012 — 108620127

CRP-01-08-0013 — 108410136

CRP-01-08-0014 — 108720145

CRP-01-08-0015 — 108110154

CRP-01-08-0016 — 108820163

CRP-01-08-0017 — 108220172

CRP-01-08-0018 — 108320181

CRP-01-08-0019 — 108610196

CRP-01-08-0020 — 108530205

01-09 Digestive Regulation

CRP-01-09-0001 — 109120014

CRP-01-09-0002 — 109220027

CRP-01-09-0003 — 109310035

CRP-01-09-0004 — 109420046

CRP-01-09-0005 — 109520053

CRP-01-09-0006 — 109620069

CRP-01-09-0007 — 109710076

CRP-01-09-0008 — 109810088

CRP-01-09-0009 — 109230094

CRP-01-09-0010 — 109320103

CRP-01-09-0011 — 109530114

CRP-01-09-0012 — 109620127

CRP-01-09-0013 — 109410136

CRP-01-09-0014 — 109720145

CRP-01-09-0015 — 109110154

CRP-01-09-0016 — 109820163

CRP-01-09-0017 — 109220172

CRP-01-09-0018 — 109320181

CRP-01-09-0019 — 109610196

CRP-01-09-0020 — 109530205

01-10 Cardiovascular Stability

CRP-01-10-0001 — 110120014

CRP-01-10-0002 — 110220027

CRP-01-10-0003 — 110310035

CRP-01-10-0004 — 110420046

CRP-01-10-0005 — 110520053

CRP-01-10-0006 — 110620069

CRP-01-10-0007 — 110710076

CRP-01-10-0008 — 110810088

CRP-01-10-0009 — 110230094

CRP-01-10-0010 — 110320103

CRP-01-10-0011 — 110530114

CRP-01-10-0012 — 110620127

CRP-01-10-0013 — 110410136

CRP-01-10-0014 — 110720145

CRP-01-10-0015 — 110110154

CRP-01-10-0016 — 110820163

CRP-01-10-0017 — 110220172

CRP-01-10-0018 — 110320181

CRP-01-10-0019 — 110610196

CRP-01-10-0020 — 110530205

01-11 Pain Signal Modulation

CRP-01-11-0001 — 111120014

CRP-01-11-0002 — 111220027

CRP-01-11-0003 — 111310035

CRP-01-11-0004 — 111420046

CRP-01-11-0005 — 111520053

CRP-01-11-0006 — 111620069

CRP-01-11-0007 — 111710076

CRP-01-11-0008 — 111810088

CRP-01-11-0009 — 111230094

CRP-01-11-0010 — 111320103

CRP-01-11-0011 — 111530114

CRP-01-11-0012 — 111620127

CRP-01-11-0013 — 111410136

CRP-01-11-0014 — 111720145

CRP-01-11-0015 — 111110154

CRP-01-11-0016 — 111820163

CRP-01-11-0017 — 111220172

CRP-01-11-0018 — 111320181

CRP-01-11-0019 — 111610196

CRP-01-11-0020 — 111530205

01-12 Neuroplasticity Reinforcement

CRP-01-12-0001 — 112120014

CRP-01-12-0002 — 112220027

CRP-01-12-0003 — 112310035

CRP-01-12-0004 — 112420046

CRP-01-12-0005 — 112520053

CRP-01-12-0006 — 112620069

CRP-01-12-0007 — 112710076

CRP-01-12-0008 — 112810088

CRP-01-12-0009 — 112230094

CRP-01-12-0010 — 112320103

CRP-01-12-0011 — 112530114

CRP-01-12-0012 — 112620127

CRP-01-12-0013 — 112410136

CRP-01-12-0014 — 112720145

CRP-01-12-0015 — 112110154

CRP-01-12-0016 — 112820163

CRP-01-12-0017 — 112220172

CRP-01-12-0018 — 112320181

CRP-01-12-0019 — 112610196

CRP-01-12-0020 — 112530205

01-13 Sensory Processing Calibration

CRP-01-13-0001 — 113120014

CRP-01-13-0002 — 113220027

CRP-01-13-0003 — 113310035

CRP-01-13-0004 — 113420046

CRP-01-13-0005 — 113520053

CRP-01-13-0006 — 113620069

CRP-01-13-0007 — 113710076

CRP-01-13-0008 — 113810088

CRP-01-13-0009 — 113230094

CRP-01-13-0010 — 113320103

CRP-01-13-0011 — 113530114

CRP-01-13-0012 — 113620127

CRP-01-13-0013 — 113410136

CRP-01-13-0014 — 113720145

CRP-01-13-0015 — 113110154

CRP-01-13-0016 — 113820163

CRP-01-13-0017 — 113220172

CRP-01-13-0018 — 113320181

CRP-01-13-0019 — 113610196

CRP-01-13-0020 — 113530205

01-14 Breath & Autonomic Regulation

CRP-01-14-0001 — 114120014

CRP-01-14-0002 — 114220027

CRP-01-14-0003 — 114310035

CRP-01-14-0004 — 114420046

CRP-01-14-0005 — 114520053

CRP-01-14-0006 — 114620069

CRP-01-14-0007 — 114710076

CRP-01-14-0008 — 114810088

CRP-01-14-0009 — 114230094

CRP-01-14-0010 — 114320103

CRP-01-14-0011 — 114530114

CRP-01-14-0012 — 114620127

CRP-01-14-0013 — 114410136

CRP-01-14-0014 — 114720145

CRP-01-14-0015 — 114110154

CRP-01-14-0016 — 114820163

CRP-01-14-0017 — 114220172

CRP-01-14-0018 — 114320181

CRP-01-14-0019 — 114610196

CRP-01-14-0020 — 114530205

01-15 Biological Baseline Reset

CRP-01-15-0001 — 115120014

CRP-01-15-0002 — 115220027

CRP-01-15-0003 — 115310035

CRP-01-15-0004 — 115420046

CRP-01-15-0005 — 115520053

CRP-01-15-0006 — 115620069

CRP-01-15-0007 — 115710076

CRP-01-15-0008 — 115810088

CRP-01-15-0009 — 115230094

CRP-01-15-0010 — 115320103

CRP-01-15-0011 — 115530114

CRP-01-15-0012 — 115620127

CRP-01-15-0013 — 115410136

CRP-01-15-0014 — 115720145

CRP-01-15-0015 — 115110154

CRP-01-15-0016 — 115820163

CRP-01-15-0017 — 115220172

CRP-01-15-0018 — 115320181

CRP-01-15-0019 — 115610196

CRP-01-15-0020 — 115530205

Appendix C — Sequential Allocation Rules

CRP Structural Codes™ System

C1. Purpose of Sequential Allocation

Sequential allocation ensures:

- Clean expansion of subsystems without renumbering
- Predictable indexing in print and digital formats

- Stable cross-referencing between Index and Entries
- Consistent internal structure across all volumes

The system is built so **growth never breaks order**.

C2. Allocation Unit

Allocation is performed **within a subsystem**.

Each subsystem receives a contiguous block of variants:

VVV = 001 → 020 (standard reference layer)

This is the default for 20-entry subsystem builds.

C3. Core Rules

Rule 1 — Variant Allocation is Sequential
Within any subsystem, variants are assigned:

001, 002, 003 ... 020

No skipping. No rearranging.

Rule 2 — Variants Do Not Repeat Within a Subsystem
Each variant value is unique inside its subsystem.

Rule 3 — Subsystems Do Not Share Variant Identity
Variants can repeat across subsystems (because subsystem ID changes), but the full structural code remains unique.

Rule 4 — Function and Intensity Are Assigned Independently
Variant number does not determine function or intensity.
Variant is a slot. Function/intensity is classification.

Rule 5 — Check Digit is Derived Only from Variant
Under Option B, validation uses the VC-20 cycle keyed to Variant (VVV).
This gives predictable integrity checks at scale.

C4. Standard 20-Entry Subsystem Allocation Template

Each subsystem contains 20 entries.

Recommended balanced composition:

- Stabilize (1) — 2 entries
- Increase (2) — 3 entries
- Decrease (3) — 3 entries
- Repair (4) — 2 entries
- Protect (5) — 3 entries
- Amplify (6) — 3 entries
- Recalibrate (7) — 2 entries
- Accelerate (8) — 2 entries

Total = 20

This balance prevents a subsystem from becoming "all acceleration" or "all protection."

C5. Intensity Allocation Guidance (Standard)

Recommended intensity split per 20-entry subsystem:

- Class I — 6 entries
- Class II — 11 entries
- Class III — 3 entries
- Class IV — 0 (reserved)

This keeps the system usable for beginners while retaining high-intensity tools.

C6. Expansion Layers (Future Growth)

To expand a subsystem beyond 20 entries, allocation continues sequentially:

Primary Reference Layer

- 001–020

Expansion Layer

- 021–060

Specialist Layer

- 061–120

High-Density Layer

- 121–200

Long-Horizon Reserved Capacity

- 201–999

No existing code changes when expanding.
New entries append forward.

C7. Subsystem Entry Numbering (Catalog ID)

Book navigation uses Catalog IDs:

CRP-01-02-0001 → CRP-01-02-0020

Rules:

- Always 4 digits for entry number
- Always pad with zeros
- Catalog numbering resets per subsystem

This prevents confusion during edits and reprints.

C8. Ordering Rules Inside the Book

Within each subsystem:

1. Entries are printed in ascending variant order:
   001 → 020
2. The Functional Index provides alternative lookup paths.
3. The Numerical Index provides absolute lookup.

Primary reading experience = sequential.
Search experience = index-driven.

C9. Cross-Volume Consistency Rule

All volumes must follow:

- Same variant allocation logic
- Same functional categories
- Same intensity tiers
- Same check-digit method

This ensures the series operates as a single unified reference system.

Appendix D — Intensity Distribution Matrix

D1. Purpose of the Intensity Matrix

Intensity is not a "power level."

It is a **stability management control**.

The Intensity Distribution Matrix ensures:

- The system remains usable for beginners
- High-intensity entries remain limited and intentional
- Subsystems stay balanced and not destabilizing
- The reference manual feels engineered, not random

D2. Intensity Classes (System Definition)

Class I — Gentle Calibration (I = 1)
Low load. Baseline-friendly. Used for stability building, minor correction, and daily discipline.

Class II — Standard Structural Activation (I = 2)
Primary operating tier. Most entries live here. Designed for consistent controlled use.

Class III — High-Intensity Structural Shift (I = 3)
Reserved. Limited quantity. Used when stability is established and a stronger shift is required.

Class IV — Reserved (I = 4)
Not used in standard volumes. Reserved for advanced structural calibration volumes.

D3. Standard Distribution Per Subsystem (20 Entries)

Default 20-entry subsystem intensity distribution:

- **Class I:** 6 entries
- **Class II:** 11 entries
- **Class III:** 3 entries
- **Class IV:** 0 entries

Total: 20

This is the baseline matrix for all subsystems.

D4. Standard Distribution Per Domain (300 Entries Example)

For a 15-subsystem domain with 300 entries:

- **Class I:** 90 entries
- **Class II:** 165 entries
- **Class III:** 45 entries
- **Class IV:** 0 entries

This creates an engineered density curve:

Most entries = Class II
Support layer = Class I
Pressure tools = Class III

D5. Function × Intensity Placement Rules

Intensity should not be distributed randomly.

Recommended placement logic:

Class I

- Decrease (3)
- Recalibrate (7)
- Accelerate (8) (limited)
- Repair (4) (light resets)

Class II

- Stabilize (1)
- Increase (2)
- Amplify (6)
- Protect (5)
- Repair (4)

Class III

- Protect (5) (hard lock entries)
- Increase (2) (surge entries)
- Amplify (6) (capacity jump entries)
- Decrease (3) (deep reduction entries, used sparingly)

Avoid assigning Class III to every function inside a subsystem. Class III must remain controlled.

D6. Subsystem Integrity Rule (No Overload)

Per 20-entry subsystem:

- Maximum Class III entries: **3**
- Maximum concurrent Class III usage (recommended): **1**
- Never stack multiple Class III entries unless stability is confirmed.

The book must communicate discipline and stability control.

D7. Domain-Specific Overrides (Allowed)

Some domains naturally require more stabilization.

Examples:

Biological / Nervous System domains

- Can increase Class I count slightly (7–8) if needed
- Must keep Class III controlled

Financial Optimization domains

- Can support slightly more Class III entries in certain subsystems (e.g., Debt Freedom, Revenue Acceleration)
- Still capped to avoid "all accelerator" perception

Overrides must remain consistent across that domain.

D8. Print-Index Implementation

The Intensity Index lists codes numerically grouped by:

Class I
Class II
Class III
(Class IV reserved)

This allows:

- Quick selection by stability readiness
- Safer reader navigation
- Less misuse of higher intensity entries

Appendix E — Cross-Subsystem Stacking Guidelines

CRP Structural Codes™ System

E1. Purpose of Stacking

Stacking is not additive power.

Stacking is **system loading**.

The goal is to:

- Maintain stability while applying change
- Prevent overload and volatility
- Avoid contradictory sequences running simultaneously
- Increase consistency of results through controlled structure

---

E2. Hard Limits (Non-Negotiable)

Maximum concurrent sequences: 3
Maximum Class III sequences at once: 1
Maximum total daily sessions: 2 (standard)

If stability is low, reduce to:

- 1–2 sequences total
- Class I or Class II only

E3. The Standard Stack (Default)

Use this stack pattern as the base for most readers:

1. **Stabilize (1)**
2. **Increase (2) or Amplify (6)**
3. **Protect (5) or Recalibrate (7)**

This creates:

Base stability → forward pressure → containment

E4. The Overload Stack (When Life Is Heavy)

Use this when stress or dysregulation is high:

1. **Decrease (3)**
2. **Stabilize (1)**
3. **Protect (5)**

This creates:

Load reduction → baseline anchoring → boundary protection

Avoid Accelerate in overload states.

E5. The Recovery Stack (After a Crash)

Use this when recovery is the goal:

1. **Repair (4)**
2. **Stabilize (1)**
3. **Amplify (6)**

This creates:

Reset → steady baseline → restore capacity

E6. The Performance Stack (Only When Stable)

Use this when baseline is stable and capacity is strong:

1. **Stabilize (1)**
2. **Amplify (6)**
3. **Accelerate (8)**

Rule: Accelerate is only used after stabilization.

E7. Intensity Stacking Rules

Rule 1 — Never stack two Class III entries.
Even if they "feel good," it increases volatility.

Rule 2 — If you run Class III, keep the other two entries Class I or II.
Class III must be buffered.

Rule 3 — Class I is not weak.
Class I builds durability and reduces fragility.

E8. Conflict Rules (What Not to Stack)

Avoid stacking:

- **Increase + Decrease** in the same subsystem at the same time
- Multiple Accelerate entries together
- Multiple Protect entries together (creates rigidity and anxiety loops)
- High-intensity Decrease + High-intensity Accelerate
- Anything that makes you "revved up" when stability is the goal

The system is designed for controlled change, not emotional spikes.

E9. Cross-Subsystem Compatibility Rule

Stack across different subsystems when possible.

Example (Volume II):

- Sleep Architecture (01-02)
- Stress Hormone Stabilization (01-03)
- Breath Regulation (01-14)

This creates a coherent support structure without overloading one subsystem.

E10. Timing Guidelines

Morning (optional):
Stabilize / Increase / Protect
(Used for baseline and daytime capacity.)

Evening:
Decrease / Stabilize / Protect
(Used for downshift and recovery.)

Avoid running Accelerate within 4 hours of intended sleep time.

E11. Reader Safety Language (Print-Ready)

If a sequence increases agitation, nervous energy, or insomnia:

1. Stop stacking immediately
2. Drop to 1–2 entries
3. Use Decrease + Stabilize only for 48 hours
4. Resume progression only after stability returns

The system prioritizes stability over intensity.

Appendix F — Scaling Framework (Summary)

CRP Structural Codes™ System

F1. Purpose

This appendix defines how the CRP Structural Codes™ system scales to **2,500+ entries** without breaking:

- code order
- index integrity
- classification logic
- cross-volume navigation

Once published, codes remain fixed. Scaling adds forward.

F2. Core Principle

Scaling occurs by **expanding subsystems and domains**, not by rewriting code blocks.

No renumbering. No restructuring. No back-editing.

F3. Approved Scaling Methods

Method 1 — Add New Volumes (Preferred)
Each volume introduces new domains while keeping the same DDSSFI structure and validation logic.

Method 2 — Add Subsystems Within a Domain
When a domain needs deeper coverage, add subsystems (e.g., 05-24, 05-25…). Existing codes stay unchanged.

Method 3 — Expand Variants Within a Subsystem
Subsystems expand by extending VVV sequentially:

001–020 (Reference Layer)
021–060 (Expansion Layer)
061–120 (Specialist Layer)
121–200 (High-Density Layer)
201–999 (Reserved Capacity)

F4. Scale Model (2,500 Entry Blueprint)

Two approved scaling structures:

Model A (Cleanest)
10 Domains × 25 Subsystems × 10 Variants = **2,500 entries**

Model B (Series-Optimized)
8 Domains × 25 Subsystems × 12–13 Variants ≈ **2,500 entries**

Both models preserve consistent indexing and reader navigation.

F5. Density Control Rules

Scaling must increase **utility**, not filler.

Maintain engineered distribution:

- Class II remains dominant
- Class III remains limited
- Functional categories remain balanced per subsystem
- New entries append forward only

F6. Continuity Rule (Non-Negotiable)

All future volumes must retain:

- the DDSSFI structural format
- Option B check-digit validation
- function definitions (1–8)
- intensity classes (I–III, IV reserved)
- mechanical naming conventions

A reader should open any volume and instantly understand retrieval.

F7. Outcome

When scaled correctly, the CRP Structural Codes™ series becomes:

- a defensible proprietary reference system
- a stable indexed codex at 1,500–2,500+ entries
- an expandable architecture that never breaks navigation

www.ingramcontent.com/pod-product-compliance
Lightning Source LLC
Chambersburg PA
CBHW051720160626
46733CB00060B/1199